HOW TO TRAIN YOUR HOOMAN
a field guide

*by Finnegan Count Smooshie Tushie
as transcribed by Gwen Romack*

illustrated by: Julie Goldman

Published by Off Leash Press

For information contact Gwen Romack:
thesquishyone@thefinnchronicles.com

ISBN: 978-1-7352473-2-8

I dedicate this book to all the rescue dogs out in the field, saving hoomans and working to make the world a happier, cuter place.

Also, bacon.

Table of Contents

introduction

MY NAME IS Finnegan Count Smooshie Tushie, but I go by Finn for short. I'm a mix of the regal and intense Hungarian Vizsla, the vocal and opinionated Beagle and the sensitive and stubborn Pittie. Basically, a perfect combination of intensity, volume and adorableness!

As a top graduate of the K9 Rescue Academy, I was given some really difficult hoomans for my rescue assignment. It's been a challenge training these hoomans, but I've come to love them. I've got a hairy hooman I call Daddy and a squishy one I call Mommy.

This book is a summary of key training techniques for dogs unable to attend the academy or who weren't paying enough attention when they did. (I'm talking to you, Phineas McNubbins, and Captain Wigglebutt.) **I've carefully developed these techniques and curated the most helpful strategies and practical how-to guidance into this field guide for dogs.**

I know my other books have lots of cute pictures and adorable stories that cater to the hoomans, but this book is not that. **This**

book is for the dogs. This book is a down and dirty, real-world study of the rescue creatures we tirelessly manage, save and train every day.

You can expect a raw and honest depiction of life with these confusing and gullible creatures and actionable ways you can start improving your standard of living today. We'll discuss techniques for effective training, how to handle conflict, how to manage stress and various challenges like baffs and beach chickens. After reading this book, you will know how to:

1. Train your hoomans to **properly serve** and respect you;
2. Protect, nurture and support your hoomans through life's challenges and dangers;
3. Condition your hoomans to **comply with your every wish**, "just so"; and
4. Maximize treats and minimize baffs.

Because I know pictures and videos can be helpful teaching tools, I've also created a <u>Field Guide Companion page on my website</u>. There you can find pictures and videos of these techniques in action.

THE SECRET PASSWORD IS: #imwithfinn
https://thefinnchronicles.com/field-guide

You can find my series, *The Finn Chronicles,* online at Amazon, Barnes & Noble, on my website, at most indie bookstores and some libraries. Reading these books first will give you a sense of my rescue backstory, my sarcastic charm and delightful wit. They include pictures of my gorgeous face and many facial expressions as well as links to videos that illustrate much of what we'll discuss in this training guide.

I've got The Squishy One doing the social media for me and a YouTube channel where you can find videos of endless fun and cuteness. My website has all the links to find my funny books online, in stores and in libraries and see where to follow me on all the social media stuffs:
https://www.thefinnchronicles.com

user's guide – the basics

BEFORE ENGAGING with your new hoomans, it's critical to understand their basic anatomy, functions and factory settings. Understand that while they may be new to you, most are already in used condition. Some have already been trained by other dogs and may have some bad behaviors you'll need to assess and address. It can take months to correct negative behaviors, but hang in there. **#ItsWorthIt** Some do come to you in mint condition - ready to be trained exactly how you want. Let's begin with the new model and then discuss possible issues you may encounter with the fixer-uppers.
#IWishWeHadJoannaAndChipToHalpUs

basic anatomy

Hoomans come in a variety of shapes, sizes and squishiness. They also vary greatly in terms of their intelligence, usefulness and purpose. Some will be assigned to you in new/unused condition. This means you're their first dog and you can mold them to your will more easily. Some will be used. This means they've already been trained up by another dog, so you may have to help them unlearn some bad habits before learning new ones. It's amazing (see also:

horrifying) how some dogs let their hoomans just run amuck, acting like they're in charge and making most household decisions. If you land one of these hoomans, you'll have extra work to do! **#ButItsWorthIt**

But all hoomans have some standard characteristics. First, they lack even basic abilities to sense danger. They wander around the world blissfully unaware of the many threats that lurk in every corner. Some even find dangers like bunnies, bears and squirrels to be "cute." **#BlindedByTheFur**

This leads us to key feature number two. They are morons. I don't mean to be unkind and some are marginally brighter than others. **#HeavyOnTheMarginal** But, in general, they are idiots. I often wonder how they've survived as a species at all. It's imperative to remember at all times that your hoomans are morons. They cannot be trusted to adequately care for themselves. Outdoor settings present the most risk of course, but even in their own baffrooms you must monitor their safety and supervise. **#EspeciallyTheBaffrooms #WhatchaDoinInHere**

Third, hooman sniffers and lookers are horribly undeveloped. Because the hoomans are so far behind dogs in their evolution, their sense of

smell and sight are nearly useless. When you alert them to a clear and present danger 3.7 miles away when the wind is blowing from the northeast, they will ask dumb questions like, "What is it, buddy?" and, "What do you see?" Try to remember they are sniffer-blind and looker-blind and channel your frustration into an appropriate degree of pity.
#ThisIsWhatYoureHereFor

Fourth, and this is a big one, they have almost no physical prowess or stamina. You must remember this when they invite you to play, run or hunt together. Sure, it's adorable to watch them try, but remember that they are not able to run, hunt, point, jump or take on any physical task like we can. They have only two paws that touch the ground, they have no sense of direction, they lack a tail for balance, and they have no clue how to be stealthy. It's just not part of their feature set. They have to put covers on their feets just to go outside! They are basically delicate little Weeble Wobbles that can, in fact, fall down. **#AndTheyDo**
#DontForgetWhenTheLeashIsAttached

<u>my hoomans</u>

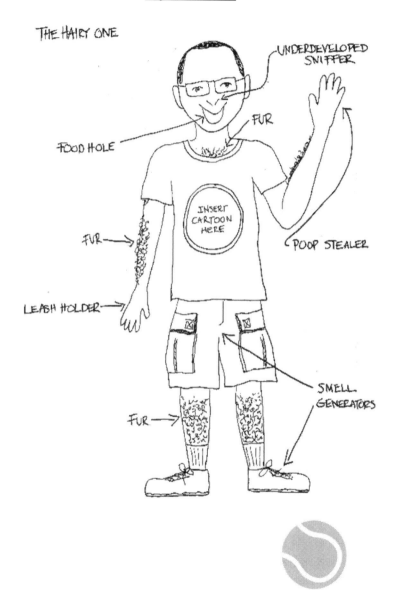

bonus hoomans

Small hoomans, known as "littles," present even more limitations in their capabilities and features. The littlest littles are called babies. They are just squirmy little blobs of confusing smells, sounds and tastes. They consume all the hoomans' attention and make wretched noises. They provide no value other than occasionally pleasant gas emissions. They are basically loud and attention-grabbing poopourri. And, apparently, it's perfectly fine for them to poop wherever they want, but we can't.
#HoomansMakeNoSense

The baby hoomans eventually grow into fun-sized littles that can prove more useful. When they are able to walk but not yet talk (see also: tattle), they provide ample opportunities for access to treats and fun. Fun-sized hoomans often have cookies, fruits and other snackies that they seem unable to protect from theft. Once you learn how to pry the treat from their sticky little paws without triggering their alarm sirens, the world is your teddy graham. **#AppleSlice #DontMindIfIDo** It's also important to remember not to jump on the fun-sized hoomans. This immediately triggers their alarm sirens and full-sized hoomans come running.
#NotInAGoodWay

Value-sized littles are very halpful and even moderately trainable. They are much slower and weaker than the full-sized hoomans and they often have remnants of what they were last eating on their hands or clothes. They often leave behind remnants of what they were last eating on the table or ground as well. They are a walking buffet.
#ExceptTheresNeverCrabLegsLikeTheyPromise
If you start early and remain consistent, you can teach them to sneak you items from their plate at dinner, accidentally feed you meals twice, let you outside and play with you. Most can be easily bested at games of tug, pounce, chase me and fetch. But, be careful. They know how to talk and that often leads to snitching.
#SnitchesDontGetStitchesAnymore

used vs. new

Hoomans in used condition present unique challenges and opportunities. Often, they're already trained to feed you, walk you and tend to basic dog needs. But, they're also sometimes lazy and think they are in charge. Some dogs lack the training or sophistication to train their hoomans properly. This can lead to hoomans that don't obey commands or don't think the dog is master. These used hoomans may scratch your ears up and down instead of down and up. They may try to limit your "hooman food" intake

or take away stuffies before the squeakerectomy is complete. These old behaviors must be assessed and addressed immediately if you have any chance of reconditioning your hooman. Fixer-upper hoomans require more work, but can be even more rewarding.
#IPromisedIWasntGonnaCryOnRevealDay

helpful features

There are some wonderful qualities about most hoomans that bring great joy. These should be celebrated and rewarded as often as possible.

- **Thumbs**: these come in very handy for opening cans, bags, car doors and other hooman things that may contain yum yums or access to fun.
  #SteeringWheelsAreTrickyForPaws
  #SoAreResealableBaggies

- **Food**: once properly trained, hoomans will bring food TO YOU. Right to your face sometimes even. No more hunting and gathering for us.
  #WeHavePeopleForThat

- **Health**: in the same way it's our job to maintain our hoomans' health, they halp maintain ours. Special hoomans called Veterinarians and Vet Technicians halp us stay healthy and fix ouchies. **#ThankYouVetPeoples**

- **Emotional Support**: hoomans come in very handy for scratching those itchies you just can't reach, petting, comforting and generally loving on us. They can be a great stress-reliever at the end of a long day. **#EspeciallyWhenTheyShareTheirPopcorn**

The relationship between you and your hooman is symbiotic. It requires a careful balance of total control and adorableness on your part. You can do it!

Let's begin.

starting off on the right paw

NO MATTER THE CONDITION of your hooman(s), you must start off on the right paw from day one. Any lapses in the early days will lead to confusion, frustration and chaos down the road. The single most important thing you must do during the initial engagement is ESTABLISH DOMINANCE. I cannot underscore this enough. Everyone will settle in better once they understand the pack order.
#WhosTheAlpha
#YoureTheAlpha
#SayItWithMe

Establishing dominance can be an uncomfortable but critical process. Here are some measures that, when applied consistently, can be highly effective:

1. Using side-eye is a wonderful and low-escalation way to politely show the hoomans you are over their nonsense. Position your face to the side of them, then roll your looker over to the corner of your eye hole. Glare at them from this position with a distinct, "are you serious?"

vibe. An alternate approach is called the looker-roll. You can roll your lookers in your eye holes from one side up to the sky then back down to the other side. This is another way to show you find whatever they are doing or saying to be ridiculous. These are also appropriate when the hoomans lie. **#WhichIsOften** "That's it, bud. We don't have any more. All gone." THESE ARE ALL LIES. **#DoYouSeeWhatImSaying** I used the side-eye and looker-roll techniques so frequently in my first four months with the Squishy One and Hairy One, that very few pictures exist of me not in one of those poses. It's not my most handsomest look, but it works. **#YouHaveToSacrificeVanitySometimes**

2. Sit on, lay across, and physically dominate the hooman whenever possible. This is especially easy when they sit down in the comfy chair or on the sofa. As soon as their flat lifeless tail hits the fabric, jump up and drape yourself across them. They may resist at first, but don't give in. They may also refer to this as "cuddling." That's fine. Let them call it what they want. As long as you are on top. **#SureThisIsCuddling #WhateverGetsYouThruTheDayLady**

3. If you can't get your whole body on top of them, make sure your paw is at least on top of their arm or hand. If they move their hand on top of your paw, move your paw on top again. This is not a parlor game – do not tolerate disrespect. The female hooman may photograph this moment and post it to social media claiming you are holding paws. Let her. **#ThatMeansThePlanIsWorking**

4. If you can't physically dominate them, try to be higher in your physical presence. Position your head higher than their head and make a rigid neck so they see your majestic and imposing stature looming over them. You can also sit beside them and lean on them to show you're the boss. If you can't sit beside them, at least lie or lean on their legs or feets. **#YouAreKingOfThatMountain #Roar**

5. Control your feeding schedule. It's key that you set the rules on feeding times and protocols. Effective techniques include the stare-down, the tantrum and the bowl-ing maneuver.

   a. The stare-down comes in two varieties. The most effective is the hooman stare-down. Position yourself in front of the hooman and stare at their heads until they notice. Once they notice, lock lookers and don't break the stare no matter what they do. If this goes on more than 23.786 seconds, proceed to the tantrum technique. Without dropping looker contact, begin whimpering, chirping, howling and barking to express your displeasure. This tantrum technique will become a staple in your training toolbox throughout your life. **#TrustMe #ImAProfessional**

b. A second variation on the stare-down is to stare-down the feeding storage unit. This may be a pantry door, a bag of kibble, a bin of kibble or some other place where they store your kibble for maximum freshness. Position yourself in front of that area and stare it down until the hooman notices and comes running. This may take a while, because, as we've discussed, they are morons. **#PatienceLuke**

c. Lastly, the bowl-ing maneuvers. These are somewhat risky moves, but sometimes you have to get assertive to make your point. First, make sure you're grabbing the empty food bowl and not the water bowl. I've made this mistake before and not only was it ineffective, it got me wet. **#WetIsTheWorst** Take the empty food bowl into your mouf and parade around with it like a show girl with feathers. If that fails, take the bowl over to your hooman and fling it at them aggressively. Stomp your feets as it flies through the air to make sure they notice. Combine with a tantrum as necessary. **#ItsUsuallyNecessary**

6. Passive-aggressive pooping and peeing inside the house are also highly effective techniques. **#IPreferAggressive** I've found that making looker-contact right before you do it gets them especially riled up. It's not enough just to drop a deuce in the living room, they have to see you do it and see you not care that they are begging you not to. They have to learn that you can pee and poop whenever and wherever you want. At any time, you could unleash a torrent of used food and

water waste on their sofa. They have to remember this. **#CodeBrown**

Deploying these techniques may feel harsh or uncomfortable at first, but they are key to setting the right tone with your hoomans. The remainder of training will go much more smoothly if you can establish yourself as Alpha early on. **#StayStrong**

It's equally important to use frequent and fulsome positive reinforcement techniques. Snuggling, kissies, playing and showing excitement when they get home are all great ways to show your hoomans you appreciate them. **#AndTheyFallForItEveryTime**

on sleeping arrangements

I'VE FOUND SLEEPING ARRANGEMENTS to be among the most flexible "rules" to which the hoomans aspire. Most begin with a "no dogs in bed" rule that quickly becomes an "ok maybe tonight if you want to cuddle" rule which quickly becomes a "fine, just stay down there, ok?" rule. Before long, you're sleeping on their face or tucked into their "business end" for a great night's sleep. Some might even try to make you sleep in the fortress of solitude, aka iron dragon, aka "craaaaaaaate." Have patience and stick with it - this won't last long. But, as with the other training topics we will discuss, persistence and consistency are key. **#HowsYourHowlingVoice #WarmItUpNow**

I like my fortress of solitude well enough. It's cozy and quiet. After I stopped eating the mattresses in there, I got a super deluxe one with a fuzzy cover. **#Winning**

But I like to use my fortress on my own terms. When asked to go inside, I scream and cry like I'm on fire. I find this halps keep the hoomans off-kilter and unsure what's going on. When they come running to let me out, it also reinforces our "do what I want

when I howl" command.
#ThisIsABroadlyHalpfulCommand

My Vizsla Code of Conduct requires that I be touching my hooman (preferably skin) 24/7. This requires extra planning and management. Please also keep in mind that cuddle sessions and naps are totally different protocols.
#ButStillTouching #AndSpooning

There's more than one way to approach sleeping dominance and it often takes repetition over many nights, but here's what's worked for me:

> **Step 1**: If they ask you to go into an iron dragon, resist. Fight it, cry, howl, and carry on for as many hours as necessary until they break. **#PackASnack #SomeCanHoldOutForDays**

> **Step 2**: Some may move you to a dog bed on the floor as some kind of "compromise." DO NOT FALL FOR THIS. When your bed is on the floor you are not equal to the hoomans. **#Resist**

> **Step 3**: If outright resistance is failing, accept the dog bed compromise so you are free in the room to execute Step 4. But remember not to get too comfortable or you'll fall asleep and lose your

moment. **(PRO-TIP: I find destroying the bed on the first night establishes you mean business and also makes it less comfortable for future nights - so less risk of falling asleep on the job.) #Bonus**

Step 4: Monitor the hoomans' breathing sounds and movements. When they start snoring like chainsaws cutting through a forest, it's time. Once they're asleep they are more malleable. Approach the side of the bed with the hooman you think most likely to crack - this is usually the female hooman. Place your lookers and ear flaps into the sad "I'm just an innocent puppy, why don't you love me?" position and begin negotiations. I usually begin with a soft whimper that's quiet but loud enough for her to hear over the chainsaws. **#zzzzzzzchhhhhhzzzzzzzzz**

Step 5: If the soft whimper doesn't work or she can't hear you over the trees falling, proceed to pawing. I like to swat at her from the side of the bed. I put my two front paws up on the side of the bed and then whack her as hard as I can. If that fails, I shove my face under the edge of the blankies and buck around like a bronco. **#HeeHaw** This makes her cold and

annoyed and eager to stop the nonsense.
#JustWhereIWantHer

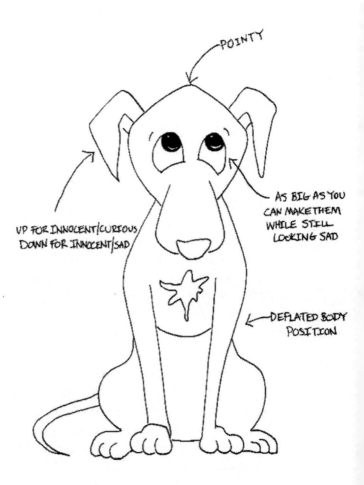

POINTY

AS BIG AS YOU
CAN MAKE THEM
WHILE STILL
LOOKING SAD

UP FOR INNOCENT/CURIOUS
DOWN FOR INNOCENT/SAD

DEFLATED BODY
POSITION

Step 6: Now, at this point, you've
hopefully lulled, guilted or annoyed her
into capitulation. Your next decision and
challenge will be location and position on

the bed. Do you want to sleep at their feets? Risky - lots of potential feets to the face issues there. Do you want to sleep between them? Probably - you can monitor both more easily and prevent any unapproved contact between them. Do you want to have a pillow of your own? Do you prefer the cinnamon roll, stiff-arm or paws-in-the-air-like-you-just-don't-care position? I find this requires some trial and error.

I often begin at her feets, wound into the smallest position possible, so she thinks this was a good idea. Once she's back at the labor camp, I work my way up to her lady business area, or as I call it, "the Bermuda triangle." It's warm and cozy, I can monitor operations from the cinnamon roll position and the blankies block out the environmental noises emanating from their power tools. (Though the blankies do trap the fume-pollution, if you know what I mean.) But, it's easy to get lost in there. After a while, it gets too hot and humid inside the triangle and I wake up fighting for oxygen. It's then that I crawl my way slowly up to the armpit area and begin in the cuddle-bug position. It's also delightfully smelly and warm, but closer access to oxygen from outside the blankies. I enjoy lulling her back to sleep in the "awwww, you wanna cuddle baby?" position. I tuck myself into her side and allow her to pet me and hold me like a poopouri hooman. Then, once I hear, "timber," I shoot my arms out like iron posts with pointy spikes designed to keep the enemy from breaching the castle walls. **#ComeAtMeBro**

This stiff-arm position has several benefits. First, it allows for ventilation to all my armpits and my belly. I like a cool breezy belly situation. Second, I'm once again establishing my place as Alpha by taking up as much space as possible. Third, once the arms are in their full-upright locked position - like legs on a 1970's folding table - no one can make them fold down.
#JustPushInThatClipThing #NoTheSpring #HereLetMeDoit

Disclaimer: Mommy says I am legally obligated at this time to advise you that she does not snore, ever. It is only Daddy that operates heavy machinery at night. Accordingly, she also has no equipment that releases fumes of any kind. She is as dainty as the day is long.

#AlsoIHaveABridgeForSaleAtABargainPr
ice #CallMe

Step 7: Now, this next part is critical. At or
before sunrise, it's imperative that you
pounce on one of their faces to a) alert
them to brekkie time and b) reward them
for their good decision to let you stay in
bed. **#PositiveReinforcementIsKey**

As you progress in your training and
sophistication, you'll be able to influence more
features of sleeping arrangements. I find I prefer
a summer weight down comforter and higher
thread count sheets - Egyptian cotton, only.
#IMightBeASheetSnob

singing the song of our people

I MENTIONED EARLIER the important and ubiquitous "do what I want when I howl" command. This is also sometimes known as the "recall" command. It's important that you have a way to make the hoomans come running whenever you want. This command can also be used to express your displeasure at their lackluster service or failure to meet your needs. #ReserveForTwoStarsOrLess

The desired behavior is established through a variable pattern of howling fits that leave the hooman wondering what's wrong and eager to serve you. **#MakeItSoNumberOne**

Begin with occasional, infrequent and random howlings (see also: concerts) when they are in another room. Point your face to the sky for optimal acoustics. Really tighten your diaphragm and open your throat so the sound carries as far as possible without straining your vocal cords.
#VocalResonanceIsKey #ProjectionIsToo

#JustAskBocelli #DramaCamp #FromTheDiaphragm

I find if you overuse this command or don't give them appropriate reinforcement upon compliance, it loses its effectiveness and can even lead to a certain female hooman making videos while laughing at you and posting them on YouTube. But I digress. **#SorryWhereWasI**

For at least the first five times, be sure to roll on your back and look afraid and pitiful when they approach. When they rub your belly and tell you everything is ok, perk up like they just saved you. This ruse is important to them feeling like rushing to your aid was worth it. You may really need their thumbs to halp save you one day. **#PreparednessBadge**

Over time, concerts can also become an effective protest mechanism if you start them when the hoomans are already in the room. Failure to begin dinner preparation at precisely dinner o'clock: protest concert. Failure to provide your after-dinner pill pocket: protest concert. Failure to halp you get treats out of the evil rubber toy: protest concert. Something foreign sitting in the hallway that wasn't there before: protest concert. These are all acceptable uses to express your displeasure with your hooman and signal that you demand action.

Note: we will devote an entire chapter to retaliation techniques, but keep howling in mind as a good one for 4 a.m. payback for laughing at your protest videos and posting to YouTube. #NowWhosLaughingSquishyOne

what's that? i can't hear you, hooman.

SELECTIVE LISTENING is another highly-effective tool in your toolkit. Unlike many of the other techniques, you may use this one with reckless abandon.
#ThatMeansWheneverYouWant

Selective listening requires effective acting. Rely on your theatre training from drama camp to maximize your results. You'll need to pull off convincing deafness and shock at their shock that you couldn't hear them just then.
#WaitDidYouSaySomething #OhIDidntHearYou
#ComeCloserAndTellMeAgain
#DramaCampWasWorthEveryPenny

Here are some great ways you can deploy this tactic in the field:

- **Treat management**: The primary goal of any dog-hooman relationship is to create an environment that promotes maximum treatage. **#TreatsAreLife** One great way to promote frequent and automatic treatage is pretending you can't hear them a lot of the time. If you only obey them when they have treats in hand, they will more frequently have treats in hand. **#ItsJustScience**

- **Laziness**: Sometimes they want you to move and you don't wanna. It might be off their lap, out of their bed, or out of their way. Consider ignoring their first five or six pleas. I find the "I'm clearly sound asleep, hooman" approach halpful here. How could you possibly get up and move when you can't even hear them asking? If they try to move you manually, follow-up with the "60-pound sack of wet concrete" maneuver. It's amazing how much heavier and immovable you become when you pull a wet-noodle/ situationally-deaf combo action.

- **Interrupting fun:** Hoomans expect you to just come running when they call you. They also expect you to stop doing something when they say, "stop" and drop something when they say, "drop." They have endless commands for ruining your fun. My hoomans constantly abuse the "leave it" command. **#YOULeaveIt #IEatWhateverIWantOffTheGround** Anyway, selective listening in these situations can often at least buy you time. Playing off-leash with your friends at the park and the hoomans call you back? Sorry, can't hear ya, Squishy. **#JustTryToCatchMe** Jumping up on a neighbor to get closer to their face for kissies and the hoomans yell, "down"? Sorry, Hairy One…can't hear you either. "Don't eat that snail, Finnnnn!!!" Mmhmmmn, you betcha, pops.

Interestingly, I find the hoomans double down on treats when I act my worst and deafest. They seem to believe I need retraining to re-establish active listening behaviors. **#TwistMyPaw**

you can vomit anytime you want

IT'S A SCIENTIFICALLY-PROVEN fact that vomiting freaks hoomans out. So does poop. One well-timed or well-placed barf or poop can really get things hoppin'. **#AndGetThemHoppin**

This is another area that requires judicious attention to balance and frequency. Of course, a nice vomit comet or code brown can be used as retaliation, but it may create confusion when you're actually sick. I try to limit my use of this dominance technique to clearly-defined situations that are easily discerned as within my control:

- **First, we eat grass**: I like to graze on grass, grass clippings and dried grass-cakes (despite and especially because of their protestations) and then come inside and crawl into Mommy's lap for a green vomit surprise. She loves it! **#SometimesSheFindsATeenySnailInThere**

- **It's brekkie time, hoomans**: There's nothing that wakes up hoomans faster than the sound of a dog puking.

#EspeciallyIfYoureInTheirBed You don't have to go through with it, though. Just heave and haw a little like it's about to happen. . . then magically pull back when they get up.

YOU CAN DO iT!

- **You don't do what I want - I don't poop where you want**: This is to be reserved for extreme situations or the first few weeks of dominance training. When they've failed to do something important for you or important to their training, sometimes drastic measures are necessary. Don't forget to make looker-contact before you drop the payload. Also remember that carpeting is much harder to clean than solid surfaces.
#SoGoForTheCarpe ting

#DoublesTheImpact

It's unclear why hoomans are so averse to vomit
and other bodily fluids. **#EspeciallyBootyJuice**
But you can use it to your advantage.
#UseTheToolsYouHave

maximizing treatage

AS YOU KNOW, treats are life. In this chapter, we'll look at proven ways to get more treats out of impromptu situations. **#TreatageIsANoun #AndAVerb #FYI**

The hoomans will use treats to try to train us and it's a good idea to let them think that's working. **#MoreTrainingEqualsMoreTreats** We've already talked about how to use selective listening for increased treatage. Here are some other ways to optimize treatage in other everyday situations:

- **Cameras**: Anytime you see a phone or camera pointed at you or your general direction. . . get deaf and dumb, quick! These are high-stakes moments for the hoomans, especially the females. They are trying to get just the right picture or video of you to post on social media. **#AndTakeCreditForYourCuteness** Don't let the moment go to waste. They will make silly noises to try to get you to look at the camera. Don't do it until you see the treat in hand. **#SometimesTheyPreten**

dTheyHaveOneAndDont
#ThisIsWhyIHaveTrustIssues They may also call your name or tell you to "watch me." Nope.
#ShowMeTheTreatAndIllShowYouMy Cuteness

- **Cameras plus costumes**: If you see them coming with any kind of costume, accessory or hat. . . you've hit the jackpot. This is really a three-cherries-in-a-row on the machine if you pull the handle just right situation.
#DingDingDing Clothing and accessories mean not only do they want a picture, but it's also time-sensitive. Oh, is Valentine's Day tomorrow and you need this picture of me holding a rose in my teeth right nowwwwww? Interesting.
#MilkThatForAllItsWorth
#YOUSayCheeseHooman
#AlsoShowMeTheCheeseFirstPlease
Also, don't forget to squint and move a lot so the first images are blurry. Do-overs mean more treats.
#OKLetsTryOneMoreTime Try to resist

falling for the "do you wanna?" question my Mommy uses to trick me into my signature cute-face/head-tilt/blue-steel look. It's so hard, because I always wanna. Lastly, DOUBLE DOWN if you hear them say "YouTube" or "Video." Those are moving pictures that are apparently much harder to get right. So, the do-over opportunities are huge. **#Huuuuuge**

- **Kongs and other tools of the devil**: Hoomans will frequently trap treats, peanut butter or yogurt yummies inside rubber "toys" designed to keep us entertained. Someone somewhere decided we would like this. I don't know how they've come to believe this is an acceptable practice. I urge you to stop falling for this ploy. **#YoureJustMakingItWorse** Demand that they pull the treats out for you and feed you by hand. This is another ideal opportunity for a protest pop-up concert.

- **Sympathy treats**: Anytime you sense the hoomans feeling sorry for you or worried for any reason, place your ears and lookers in the "I'm just an innocent puppy why don't you love me?" position. This will often lead to a small burst of treatage. They step on your paw when you were crossing in front of them in the kitchen as they carried a hot pan of water... yelp for treatage. You're sad because your favorite hooman is away on a trip. . . sympathy treatage. They yelled at you when you did something bad. . . double down for the treatage. **#PuppyEyesAreKey**

delicious or suspicious?

DOGS ARE FREQUENTLY confronted with the delicious or suspicious dilemma. I don't have especially halpful advice here other than to do your best and assess each situation as it comes. **#ThereWillBeSomeGagging**

I find the most frequent situations calling for a delicious or suspicious decision on my part are neighbors and foodstuffs.

While on my daily patrol at the front door or front window, I often see hoomans walking past to go to the awful-horrible-no-good "pool" (see also: outside bafftub). I will never understand why they subject themselves to the pool, but it's always full of hoomans over there. Especially fun-sized and value-sized littles. As they pass to and fro, I'm obligated to size up each one to determine if they look suspicious or delicious. If they look delicious, I make a mental note to try to find them on a walk later and get in some kisses. If they look suspicious, I'm obligated to bark to mark my territory. I also have to make these decisions during walkies.
We pass a lot of hoomans on our walks and each has the potential to be delicious. **#OrSuspicious**

I've found a few universal truths in my years of decision-making:

1. Fun-sized littles are ALWAYS delicious. **#AndUsuallySticky**

2. Anytime your hooman is on an important work phone call - the passersby are automatically suspicious and require extensive and protracted barking. **#YoureWelcome**

3. The more they fight me and act nervous about me jumping up for tasting/kissies, the more I want them. What deliciousness are they trying to keep from me? **#IsItPeanutButter**

The second application of this test will come into play with hooman foodstuffs. My Mommy finds it endlessly entertaining to give me a new foodstuff and video my reaction. She has dozens of "Finn vs. _____" videos showing my decisioning in process. "Finn vs. broccoli" and "Finn vs. apples," and so on. **#ShesSoEasilyAmused**

I'm generally a protein and sugar-oriented dog. I've heard rumors from the academy that some dogs actually like vegetables. **#Blecghk** So far, I have not enjoyed broccoli, lettuce, carrots, cauliflower, kale or bell peppers. I have enjoyed watermelon (but only when they hold it for me to nibble), apples (but only when peeled just so), frozen dairy slop (more on that later), hard boiled eggies, scrambled eggies, all eggies, bacon, poultry and fowl of all kinds, fish (the stinkier the better), steak and whipped cream (reminds me of frozen dairy slop; can't put my paw on why).

My hoomans are chintzy with the extra foodstuffs and cannot be trusted, anyway. Each "wanna try this" moment is risky and may lead to gagging and spitting it out. Never swallow it if you don't like it! This confuses the hoomans. Make a big loud point of chewing it into tiny, hard to pick up pieces, spitting it out and carrying on a while about not liking it (smack your lips, lick your face or the floor, run for water to get the awful taste out of your mouf).
#AnotherGreatUseForDramaCampTraining

I insisted on trying to drink the Squishy One's coffee for months and several times made her spill it down her shirt as she tried to evade my licker. It smells awful, but she seems to love it, so I feel like I'm missing something. I'm still working on getting a taste.
#IllKeepYouPosted

I have no universal truths to offer in the foodstuffs delicious or suspicious realm. But I can offer these observations:

- Foodstuffs that come from the cold box thing are more likely to be vegetables, fruit or meat.

- Foodstuffs that come from the hot box thing on the deck are more likely to be delicious meats that you should absolutely try to taste test.

- Foodstuffs that come from wrinkly, crinkly, plasticky, crunchy bags are almost always a win.

- Foodstuffs that come from the Dairy Queen are ALWAYS A WIN.

Now, let's discuss frozen dairy slop.
#AKATheMeaningOfLife

frozen dairy slop

I LOVE FROZEN DAIRY SLOP. My lookers get huge and I shake a little when I see it or go into a place where I know I can get it. I really and truly love it. **#ItCompletesMe**

I love frozen dairy slop so much it gets its own chapter. I discovered frozen dairy slop quite by accident in 2018. I've been on a quest ever since to figure out from whence it comes and how to get more. This is optional of course, but you should really consider getting your hoomans to get you some frozen dairy slop. **#LifeChanging** I'll tell you everything I know so far to halp you in your cause.

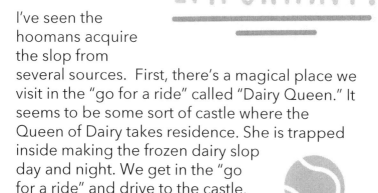

I've seen the hoomans acquire the slop from several sources. First, there's a magical place we visit in the "go for a ride" called "Dairy Queen." It seems to be some sort of castle where the Queen of Dairy takes residence. She is trapped inside making the frozen dairy slop day and night. We get in the "go for a ride" and drive to the castle. We pull up to a window and tell the nice hoomans we're there for the slop AND THEY BRING IT TO YOU. They just hand it over like it's worthless to them. They don't growl or try to defend their high value treat at all. **#Madness**

Then Mommy or Daddy holds it for me to lick and lick and lick until I look too dizzy. Mommy calls this a "brain freeze" and uses that as an excuse to take it away from me. "You can have the rest later, buddy." Ugh. **#ShesTheWorst #IDontCallHerDevilWomanForNothing**

Anyway, where was I? Oh yes, Rehoboth Beach. There is another magical source of slop in Rehoboth Beach. To get there, we travel in the "go for a ride" then walk by paw along a magical concrete path until we reach the store. The path is littered with French fries, frozen dairy slop drippings, cigarette butts, fried things, dirty diapers and other culinary delights left behind by the masses. The walk takes a long time because I am legally obligated by the Beagle Code of Conduct to carefully sniff and catalogue every single smell. There's a lot of, "leave it… leave it, Finn. Finnnnn, leave ittttt." **#WhatsThatHooman #ICantHearYou**

I love it because I've got that counter-hooman wrapped around my paw! I don't know if she is the Queen or not. **#StillInvestigating** We saunter up to the counter like we own the place and I

give my best over-eager look to the nice lady. She says, "oh what would he like to sample?" and Mommy picks something. Then the lady leans over and lets me try some! Then I make my signature, "please sir may I have anutha?" face and we repeat the process. Peanut Butter Beef Parfait, don't mind if I do? Blueberry banana sundae… ok! After a while, Devil Woman usually shuts down the fun and places an order. I usually go for a fishy flavored slop with dehydrated fish or beef sprinkles. This is the one time I forgive Mommy for taking my pictures. Anything to keep her busy while I snarf. They also sell my book there and sometimes hoomans recognize me as the local celebrity I am.
#ThatGetsMeMoreTreats

I also get to see other dogs there and sometimes we even share slop. Well, usually I share their slop and they have no choice. The hoomans get so easily distracted and it's every dog for itself. **#NoMercy**

I've recently become aware of a new, even closer doggy frozen dairy slop parlor in Bethany! It also has a counter for begging and a nice lady to give me the slop! And it's only five minutes from home by "go-for-a-ride!"
#WeWillBeRegulars
#LetsGetToKnowEachOtherShall We

Lastly, and most suspiciously, I sometimes catch the hoomans eating frozen dairy slop at home. I'll just be minding my own business, licking what needs licking by the fireplace and suddenly I smell it! My beloved dairy slop. I generally charge the hooman with the speed of a racehorse and crash into their bodies to create a momentary breach in their defenses. If I'm fast enough, I can get one, sometimes two licks across the bow before I'm shoved off. **#TheresUsuallyScreaming #ButItsWorthIt** Then I end up in a "time-out" in my fortress of solitude so they can "eat in peace." We'll discuss retaliations in a later chapter. Maybe two chapters. **#TheyOftenRequireRetaliation**

One time I saw them take the frozen dairy slop out of the very cold box in the kitchen. I'm still working on a way to get that thing open to find out more. **#SoonItWillBeMine #AllMine**

walkies: problems and solutions

REMEMBER THIS: walkies are for you not for them. Do not allow them to rush you or tell you which way to walk. Do not accept hurried pee pees or insistence that you poop on demand. **#EvenThoughWeveEstablishedYouCan**

Based on a recent study of 97 bagillion million dogs, hoomans are incredibly inconsistent and insolent during walkies. **#PlusOrMinusTwoHundredPercentMarginOfError**

100% of dogs surveyed reported that their hoomans were all over the place with times, durations, speed and distance of walkies. 94.6% reported that their hoomans rush them, but that shot to 100% among Beagles and other Hounds. **#WeCantHalpIt**

87% reported their hoomans tried to steer the direction of the walkies and another 100% of Finnegan Count Smooshie Tushies reported that their hoomans don't let them eat dangerous stuff off the ground and that the Devil Woman is the worst. **#TrueStory** **#StartlingStatistics**

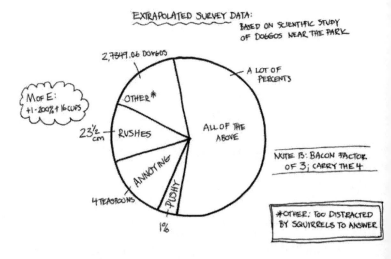

So, what can you do to curb this erratic and difficult behavior?

- **Leash management**: First, it's important to let the hoomans think the leash is for controlling you. It soothes them to think they're in charge during walkies. It's ok to let them have this one. **#EveryoneNeedsAWinSometimes** We all know we can slip out of our bonds whenever we want. Try to keep the leash secure at all times or they can wander off and get lost. Remember they have no sense of direction or danger. Outside of the house is full of potential threats to your hooman. **#StayVigilant**

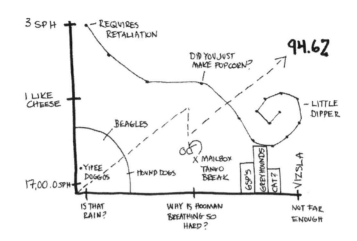

SNIFFS PER HOUR (v)

3 SPH — REQUIRES RETALIATION

94.62

DID YOU JUST MAKE POPCORN?

I LIKE CHEESE

— LITTLE DIPPER

BEAGLES

OO X MAILBOX TANKO BREAK

•YIPEE DOGGOS — HOUND DOGS

17,00.0SPH

68's   GREYHOUNDS   CAT?   VIZSLA

IS THAT RAIN?

WHY IS HOOMAN BREATHING SO HARD?

NOT FAR ENOUGH

DISTANCE (D)

- **Grass cakes and other debris**: I find I can really liven up a walk by eating something, really anything, off the ground. Grass cakes prepared by the finest lawn mowers, shot out into the yard, then cooked to perfection by the sun are always delicious. But trash, cigarette butts, dead worms, live worms, nuts and anything else I can snarf before they yoke me up on the leash is a win. "LEAVE IT, FINNNNNN!!" is what we call that game. **#AndItsABlast** It's usually followed by "Open. Opppenn. OOOOOppppppennnnnnn" where Daddy shoves his big paw in my mouf to try to snatch my treasure. I try to let him win that game a lot so he stays motivated to keep playing.

- **Evasive maneuvers**: Periodically dash right then left for no reason. If possible, cut off the hooman so they *almost* fall down. Make clear that you can trip them whenever you want. **#DidYouTrip #SeeYaNextFall**

- **Stop, drop and flop**: If they try to redirect you, speed you up or slow you down. . . stop, drop and flop. This is a clear communication that you will not be pressured into their bidding. **#WalksiesOnYourTerms**

- **The wet noodle**: If they try to pick you up or physically move you during the stop, drop and flop maneuver - deploy the wet noodle. Make your body weigh twice as much and become nearly immovable by melting into the ground around you. **#TheyWillGiveIn #JustHoldYourPosition**

- **Show me the treat**: Make sure you put lookers on a treat before you agree to any heel business. My hoomans try to trick me all the time with invisible treats they pretend to take out of their pocket. **#Resist**

Additional tips:

- Snails are delicious. We have teeny tiny ones here that tickle in my mouf. Daddy always sticks his big meaty paws into my mouf to steal them back out, but sometimes I can swallow faster than he can dental-dive.
#SometimeIPukeThemUpLater
#TwiceTheFun

- Watch out for the hoppies and jumpies. They look innocent but I'm convinced they mean us trouble. The jumpies are salty and taste bad, resist the urge to lick them. **#IHaventCaughtAHoppyYet**

- Neighbor-hoomans are awesome. I've taken mental note of the houses where my favorite neighbor-hoomans reside. During warm months, we often pass the neighbor-hoomans doing yard work or playing outside. I'm usually able to secure

prompt and agreeable lovins as soon as they see me coming. In the colder months they are not out in their yards as much and I have to work a bit harder to get them to come give me kissies. I find it halpful to deploy a basic "nuh uh, not moving right now" maneuver in the sit position and scream at their house until they come outside. It's very hard to resist the urge to jump up on the full-sized hoomans to give them better access to my primary petting zones. But, it's absolutely critical not to jump on the fun-sized and value-sized hoomans.
#TheirSirensGoOff #HoomansGetMad

- Neighbor-kitties are a gamble. I've personally never met a kitty I didn't like. But I've definitely met some that don't  like me. It's halpful to also note the houses of neighbor-kitties that could give you and your hoomans trouble during a walkie. **#ImLookingAtYouMapleTrout** Give a wide berth as you pass by and be ready to sneer, shoot dirty looks and hoof or poof as they glare at you with haughty derision. Don't show any fear or your hooman will sense weakness. **#BeBrave**

#TheyAreProfessionalGlarers
#ButYouGotThis

- Neighbor-doggies can also be a good time. But as with all dog-on-dog encounters, you must read the signs. Make note of which doggies are fun and like to be approached for walkie hellos. Whenever possible, engage in the leash-tangle-tango to give your hoomans a little extra fun. **#ChaChaCha** You go left, they go right, everybody jumps, leashes go around throats and ankles. It's so much fun. **(PRO-TIP: You can do the leash-tangle-tango solo with halp from any mailbox post, hooman leg, tree or other vertical object.)** I live for that moment of pure adrenaline when they have to drop the leash for a split instant to free you from the tangle.
  #ANYTHINGCANHAPPEN

- Obviously, the Universal K9 Code of Conduct (applicable to all breeds and breed mixes) requires that we bark at all moving things. Whether by land, air or sea, all moving creatures MUST be admonished for moving. This is especially true during early-morning or late-night walkies. The hoomans find it extra halpful when you bark your loudest and let your glorious voice ricochet around the quiet neighborhood for all to hear. **#TheyreProudIGuess** Hoppies, jumpies, tree chickens, beach chickens, Canadian air chickens, swoopy chickens, ground support chickens, beavers, squirrels (aka tree rats) and all the other mobile military commandos must be taken seriously. Warn them off with incessant barking and be sure to jump against your leash for the biggest threats. I find the squawkdrons of Canadian air chickens to be among the most dangerous. The beach chickens tend to just dive down to steal French fries or the sideways-sand-buddies while screaming "mine, mine." But they still require clear warnings. Remember that your hoomans cannot sense the inherent danger in these monsters. **#YouMustShowThem**

Don't forget to show your appreciation for great walkies to reinforce positive behaviors. This can be done by celebratory post-poop zoomies, kissies and cuddles. The hoomans also seem appreciative if you nap after a nice long walkie. Consistent positive reinforcement is key. Pavlov's dogs got him to provide a lot of treats with just a bell. **#Brilliant**

lick like your life depends on it

MANAGING THE HEALTH of your hooman is critical to your long-term survival. In this chapter, we will examine ways you can monitor both their physical and emotional health. Licking and sniffing will be your go-to tools. #ArentTheyAlways

Regular testing of your hooman's vitals is essential to understanding their immediate health situation and long-term changes. Here are some important tests that should be performed multiple times a day for each hooman.

1. **Lick like your life depends on it**: Licking plays an essential role in monitoring and managing the physical and emotional health of your hooman. Some hoomans fight licking and will attempt to shove you away. You may have to get creative in your approach. I find "drive-by" licks, brute force and persistence to be effective work-arounds when Mommy refuses to cooperate with the mandatory health management protocols outlined in this chapter. Drive-by licks require patience and

vigilance. You must lay in wait, on constant alert to seize any opportunity. I find that when she's walking by me or yacking on the phone, a small sliver of leg skin is often accessible for a quick swipe. Brute force and persistence are also important techniques, especially when used in tandem. When we're cuddling in the big comfy chair, I usually have one of her arms pinned which limits her ability to fight me. I've also found that she resists far less when she is sleeping. Fortunately, Daddy is always compliant with our testing and health goals. **#HesAGoodBoy**

- o **Salinity inspections**: It's essential that you frequently check salinity levels by licking any exposed skin you can reach. Evaluate the saltiness level and flavor through multiple licks in different areas. This process should include at least ten licks per skin sample area and be performed 256 times a day.

- o **Dietary inspections**: You should monitor the hooman's diet by frequently inspecting their recent yum yum intake. This is accomplished by licking the hooman's face and mouf shortly after you suspect yum yum consumption. For the male hoomans, also carefully inspect their shirt for additional yum yum clues.

- o **Baffing**: Unlike doggos who never ever need a single baff, ever, hoomans require frequent cleaning. At least once a day, perform a full-face cleaning and pay special attention to ears. Every other day, focus on a deep foot scrub that addresses each little piggy and the top of the foot. They do not like it when you lick the bottom of the foot and will try to squirm away. Also make note of approximately how many seconds each hooman can tolerate baffing. This is important to halp you prioritize your target areas with a better understanding of the time limits you'll be facing. **#DaddyIsTwoMins #DevilWomanIsFourSeconds**

- o **Tear removal**: Tear management and removal is performed on an as-needed basis only. Sometimes hoomans get sad and emit saline from their lookers. And it's not just the littles, either. Even the full-sized hoomans will leak tears from time to time. This is a sign of a weakened emotional state that requires your immediate attention. I recommend you drop everything and address this situation as quickly as possible. Each hooman is different in how they want to be comforted. Some will gladly receive your affection and allow you to lick away their tears. But Mommy (aka Devil Woman) frequently resists my efforts in this arena and I've found that the brute force/persistence combo technique is my only option. I pin her down and lick her face and lookers while she screams and squirms. It seems to make her feel better instantly.

2. **Use that sniffer**: You have one of the most sophisticated senses of smell in the animal kingdom. . . so use it!

   o **Pre-brekkie breathalyzer**: You should perform a pre-brekkie breathalyzer first thing in the morning on each hooman. This

can be tricky because you have to get to each one before the terrifying electric toofsbrush destroys the smell-evidence. I like to pounce on the weaker one first and shove my snout into her mouf as soon as she says, "Good morning, Finn."
#SheFallsForItEveryTime Then I quickly turn my attention to the Hairy One and usually get in a sniff-lick combo before he declares, "Enough, Finn." **#HesAGem**

- o **General funk**: Hoomans emit a variety of smells from different places on their bodies. Some are more delightful than others. I pay careful attention to the hoomans' food waste byproducts in the baffroom. There's a single moment between deposit and flush when you can sometimes catch a whiff. I sometimes try to monitor Daddy's liquid waste byproduct stream real-time but he gets really grumpy. "Back off, Finn!" "Get out of my butt, Finn." "What if it splatters, Finn?" He's so cute. I'll take the risk because his health matters that

much to me.
#SomeMightCallMeAHero

o **Gas fumes**: Much like dogs, hoomans will also emit a clear delicious-smelling gas into the air from time to time. They go by a variety of names: "boom-boom," "stink-bomb," "dropping heat," "silent-but-deadly," and "OMG what is that" to name a few. These plumes of delight provide important clues to the hooman's yum yum intake, gut health and digestive enzymes. They often change based on the content of the yum yum intake. **#ChiliNightsAreTheBest**

3. **Other vitals:**
   o **Pulse speed and rhythm**: I really only check the hoomans' heart function when they are sick. You can tell they are sick when they lay around a lot, moan and complain (more than usual), smell weird around bandages or emit strange goop from their sniffer. During these difficult times they may not want to cooperate with your oversight. Again, I find that persistence and intense desire

really halp here. I've found that laying across the hooman's neck and placing my chin on their throat gives me easy access to monitor their vitals even while I'm asleep. Resist them when they try to shove you off. **#ItsForTheirOwnGood**

- o **Smile management**: It's also important to ensure the hoomans are smiling and laughing enough times a day. If you find they have not smiled or laughed within the last hour - immediately do something adorable. Roll onto your back and play with a toy. Pounce on a toy and charge around the house with it like a lunatic. Initiate zoomies. Do something - anything - to trigger a smile. Smiles release endorphins in their weak little brains and this sends happy feelings throughout their bodies. Laughter also triggers happiness and can often be accomplished with similar feats of adorableness. **#CutenessTherapyIsAThing**

- o **Exercise**: I know I told you earlier that walkies are for you and not them. And

that's true. But walkies are also good for your hoomans' health and well-being. If you sense them getting tired or restless, demand a walkie. Get them outside to the fresh air and sunshine. Walkies can be a halpful part of a well-balanced and healthy hooman. We'll talk more in the next chapter about ways you can halp manage your hoomans' stress.
#TheyAreWoundTightArentThey

stress management

HOOMANS ARE INHERENTLY stressed-out creatures. The deck is really stacked against them in terms of their overall mental and emotional health. **#PoorDears** As is the case for doggos, stress is not good for hoomans and should be managed carefully.

causes of stress

Hoomans often suffer from thoughts and emotions related to living in past and future moments. Their ability to stay focused on the present and go with the flow is quite limited. We can halp them learn to enjoy moments as they come and focus on what matters most… us! **#AmIRight #YesIAm**

They also apparently have to do something called "work" to make the money to buy the kibble, toys and treats. At my house, the constant banging on the pooter and yacking on the phone is stressful for them (and me). Some have demanding emotional works that involves halping other people get better, doing manual labor, getting yelled at by mean bosses and doing dangerous stuff like fighting fires. **#ThankYouNiceHoomans**

The noise box also seems to trigger stress and a variety of emotions in hoomans. They watch something called "the news" on the noise box and get tense. Sometimes they watch something called "a movie" and it makes Mommy cry. **#ShesAnUglyCrier** The noise box does make them laugh from time to time, but I find it best to avoid the noise box as often as possible. I often sigh loudly and make a scene about the noise and light coming from the noise box to get them to turn it off.

<u>ways to alleviate stress</u>

There are a lot of great ways to halp the hoomans burn off their stress. Every hooman is different so you have to assess and address using techniques customized to their needs. I've found the following to prove halpful for mine:

- **Prevention**: The best cure is never getting sick! Try to prevent the stress from happening in the first place. I like to crawl up into their lap and push away the pooter or phone or block their access to the keyboard with my paws. This stops them from doing the works and focuses them on my adorable face. My hoomans work from home and this enables me to frequently disrupt their concentration on works. Recently, I've also found it helpful to paw their talkies headset thing off their faces during calls. If I can't get them off, I like to breathe loudly and sigh heavily into the talkies part and make the other hoomans think my hooman is bored or annoyed. Anything that distracts from you is a problem you should try to address.

If your hooman does works outside the home, deploy consistent and frequent guilt trips when they leave and return. Affix your ears and lookers into the "I'm just an innocent puppy, why don't you love me?" position and look as sullen as possible when they gather up their bits to leave. **(PRO-TIP: It's extra effective if you cry or howl as they walk away from the door.)**

You can also destroy stuff while they're gone but this can lead to unintended consequences. . . so, use sparingly! **#IronDragonTime**

Upon their return, be sure to greet them with extreme exuberance. **#OHMYDOGYOUREBA**

CK Clearly communicate that you thought they would never ever return and how worried you were. Try to show them a) you could've died, b) they could've died and c) they should never do this again.

- **Exercise**: We briefly discussed the value of exercise, sunshine and fresh air in the previous chapter. Exercise can come in multiple forms, depending on your hooman and your location. A little jaunt around the neighborhood is always a quick win. You can also take your hoomans on more extended excursions such as a hike through the woods, a stroll on the beach, a walk on the boardwalk, an adventure in the countryside or even go running with them. A good game of fetch or chase me can also get the hoomans' blood flowing. (Note: this has to be actual fetch, not keep-away fetch.)

- **Play**: A great way to distract your hooman from sad or stressful stuff is with play. Grab a toy and start playing with it. Pounce, run, chase, roll on and kick a toy to get their attention and show them how much fun it can be. Indicate your willingness to share your

most prized toy by assuming the
downward dog stance and wagging
your tail.

BUTT IN AIR

WAG IT LIKE
YOU MEAN IT

DON'T FORGET
TO SMILE

DOWNWARD DOG SHOWS
YOU CARE

If this fails, you may need to get
clearer in your communication. Start
by taking a toy and
dropping it at their
feets. If they don't
notice, pick it up and
drop it again. If that fails,

bang your face into their legs so they look down and see the irresistible toy. If that fails, drop the toy into their lap and assume the "I'm just an innocent puppy, why don't you love me?" pose. **#TheyCantResistIt**

An effective alternate approach the hoomans really love is to take your loudest squeakiest toy and squeak it as close to their face as possible. Over and over. Don't stop until they engage. **#TheLouderTheBetter**

- **Kissies**: When you sense the hooman is emitting stress smells or sadness smells, deploy the kissies!! Assertive kissies can be comforting to the hoomans even if they resist at first. **#KissiesShowYouCare**

- **Amp up the adorableness**: It's hard to imagine being any more adorable than you already are. But it is possible with a few clever tricks. The key is positioning yourself where the hooman will see your amped up cuteness and their brains will have no choice but to release serotonin. Obviously, the "I'm just an innocent puppy, why don't you love me?" pose is always a strong move. Huge round

lookers, lowered ears, the deep stare
into their souls. . . always a winner!

I've found the hoomans also let out
lots of "awwww" and "looook at that"
sounds when I:

- Lay on my back for belly rubs

- Lay on my back and play with a
toy

- Sleep in an awkward position
with limbs going every which
way

- Fall asleep with a toy or ball in
my mouf

- Hang off a piece of furniture in
some awkward position

- Cuddle with a piece of their
clothing (but you have to resist
the urge to chew it
#IKnowItsHard)

- Paw at their arm to get them to
pet me

- Keep pawing
when they stop

- Dig through all my toys trying to find just the right one

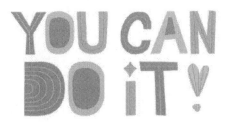

Stress management is a key part of your job as a rescue dog. You'll need to devote daily attention to this task and quite often, deploy anti-stress machinery more than once a day. **(PRO-TIP: Incorporate some of these techniques to your everyday portfolio. If you can be extra cute while catching some zzz's. . . why not!)**

keeping them on their toes

IT'S HALPFUL IF your hoomans don't get too cozy in your relationship. Yes, of course you want to have a happy and engaging relationship with your hooman. But, continued and gentle reinforcement of your position as Alpha is also important. In this chapter, we'll discuss fun ways you can keep your hooman on their toes. **#VarietyIsTheSpiceOfLife** As a special bonus, these techniques are also a load of fun for you. **#SelfCareMatters**
#FollowBreneBrownForMoreTips

- **Ghosts**: From time to time, it's great to have a little fun with them. I like to get them all riled up by alerting to ghosts and spirits in the room. There's lots of ways to do this, but I like to fixate on a spot on a blank wall and growl. Maybe put my hackles up and look alarmed. Be sure to look over at your hooman as if to say, "OMG. . . do you see it, too?" then look back. Barking and growling at nothing under the bed or in the closet can also be effective. I usually roll this one out when Daddy is away and Mommy is already feeling vulnerable alone in the house with me. She's really easy to spook.

- **Threats/Intruders**: Similar to the ghost technique, I like to alert to non-existent threats in the yard or house. I usually start by barking at the window and acting crazy like there's a grizzly out there. I might run from window to window barking for my life and begging them to look. Another way is to creep out to the living room or dining room while they are in bed and start carrying on out there. They'll jump up and come running to see what's got you shook. Hint: don't tell them.

- **Fur missiles**: Finnnnncommmmmming!!!!!!!!! Fur missiles have become a real favorite around here. I deploy a fur missile attack at least twice a week and it's a great time for everyone. I start by making sure Mommy is asleep or working on something important on her laptop from bed. Extra credit if she's holding a coffee cup. Then I position myself at the end of the runway (see also: hallway) and begin my approach. With target acquired and locked in my scope, I take off at 200 mph through the house and into the bedroom. Before she knows what's coming, I take to the air and soar across the bed like a

Tomahawk Cruise Missile. Upon impact with her body, she screams and that creates an opportunity for some health test licks. She loves how I slam into her with all my force and shower her with kisses. She screams, "nooooo. . . Finnnnnnnnnn!" but we both know she doesn't mean it.
#FurMissileOfLovesAreFun

- **Tantrums**: We've already examined how singing the song of our people in impromptu concerts can be an effective way to establish patterns and schedules with your hoomans. But, did you know they can also be combined with stomping, looker-rolling, pouting, flailing and throwing yourself on the floor to create epic tantrums? Sometimes, for no reason, I like to just throw a full-on toddler-in-a-toy-store-being-told-no level tantrum.

- **Make them look like liars**: This is a great one, but you have to pay close attention to spot the opportunities. I take any chance I can get to make them look like liars. I'll give you some examples. One time I heard Mommy talking to a trainer about how unruly and stubborn I was and how she wanted him to halp "fix me." When we arrived at his facility, I knew this was my chance to really drive her nuts. He asked her what we should work on first. She said heel. He said he wanted to start by just seeing how I handle heel and asked her to take me for a stroll. Before she could even say the command, I locked lookers with her like she was a piece of juicy sirloin. I trotted at her pace, didn't tug and kept looker-contact the whole time. **#HeelWorldChampion** She sighed in exasperation and said, "I swear this is not the same dog" while the nice man looked confused at her obvious lies and exaggerations. Another great opportunity is always the vet's office. If I'm bored and missing my vet friends, I'll fake some symptoms to get Mommy and Daddy worked up. Mommy will call and tell them all my troubles and book an appointment. **#WorksEveryTime** When I get there, I make sure there's not a symptom to be found.
#SheHasToPayAnyway #ThatsGravy

- **Shivs and shanks**: There's some debate among doggos about what's a shiv and what's a shank. For simplicity, I will refer to any knife-looking object as a shiv. I find it halpful to whittle down bones, antlers and petrified cheese bars into shivs. First, it's just plain fun. Scraping my teefs against the smooth surface until I fashion a jagged weapon. . . what could be more satisfying? Second, it seems to alarm them. I like that they know I can shiv them anytime I want. **#ItsAlsoAVerb** It's best not to wave it at them or motion towards them that you know how to use it. Just make them aware you know how to make one and can. I like to include them in the process by deploying the "hold dis" technique. **#EveryoneLikesToBeIncluded** I bring the chunk of fun to them and push it into their hand until they instinctively take it. Then I put my paws on their hands to guide it to my mouf. As I scrape and lick, I make sure to keep my nails digging into the surface of their hands just a little so they stay in line. Eventually, someone always notices it's turned into a shiv. And at that moment, the balance of power quietly shifts another small notch.

The keys to remember:

- Keep them slightly concerned and confused as often as possible.
- Push your luck (use your cuteness if you push too far.)
- You only live once. Find enjoyment in the little things.

what the bafftub?

IN THIS CHAPTER, we will explore ways to minimize, manipulate and mitigate baffs. I get it. Most of us hate baffs with the passion of a hundred burning suns. There are a few freaky dogs out there that confuse the hoomans by seeming to enjoy water and baffs. These hoomans talk to each other, guys. We need to stick together on this. **#AllTogetherNow**

Why the hoomans can't understand we have tongues for this, I will never know. But they just don't seem to get it. The best we can hope for is to minimize, manipulate and mitigate baff-time horrors. **#TheThreeMs**

- **Minimize**: Try to avoid activities that lead to baffs. It's hard because those activities are usually the most funnest of all activities.  **#MudIsFun #SandIsFun #ALLDIRTISFUN** You can try to combine dirty activities to get the most out of each baff, though. Don't settle for one romp through the sand - demand a stop at the muddy field on the way home. Going for a hike? Great! Demand a quick pull off at the bay for some stinky dead crab-shell rolls before you head back to the house. Find a skunk to antagonize! Roll in poop. The options are endless. If you know a baff is coming, get the most out of the day before it happens. **#CarpeDiem #ItsLatin #ItMeansRollInMoreDirt**

- **Manipulate**: Manipulation in general is key to any good doggo-hooman bond. Subtly is key. When they tell you to head to the horrid chamber of doom. . . skulk, go wet noodle, get rigid or do whatever you can to fight it. Please don't be one of those dogs that just gives in and cooperates! If they want to baff you, they have to carry you. Period. **#VivaLaRevolucion**

Once inside the torture closet, cooperate as little as possible and force them to be bent over and struggle the entire time. Tuck that tail down so tight they need a crow bar to get up under there. "Gimme your paw," no way! You bend over and get it yourself, hooman traitor. **#IfImWetYoureGonnaBeDizzyAndExhausted**

CAULDRON OF SORROWS

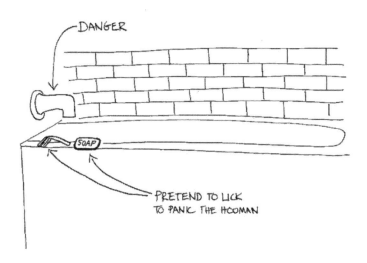

DANGER

SOAP

PRETEND TO LICK
TO PANIC THE HOOMAN

For those that get baffs in the cauldron of sorrow instead of the torture closet, you have a lot of other options available for maximum annoyance. As soon as they get you lathered up, shake your whole body with the force of a thousand tennis balls. The goal is to get the smelly lather across the room and onto their toofsbrush. This doesn't work from inside the torture closet, but you can get it into their lookers and moufs in there. Cronch down on a bottle of shampoo or try to lick the bar of soap (but don't make contact, just pretend). Oh, is that a razor you forgot to move away. . .

lemme try to get it! Obviously when they tell you to shake off the water at the end, refuse. **#YouShakeOnYourTerms**

Note: We will discuss preheated towels from the dryer in the "Creature Comforts" section, so make sure you keep reading for this delightful post-baff pro-tip.

- **Mitigate**: Mitigation is the last chance you have at trying to at least stomach the horror more peacefully. I've really only come up with one way to make the debacle more tolerable: treatage combined with licking. Once the hoomans are sleeping, log into their social media and search on "lick matts." This will make ads pop up that show them what you need. Lick matts suction to the walls of the torture closet or sides of the cauldron of sorrow. When smeared with a nice nut butter or yogurt, they can be soothing escapes during the awfulness. I find licking really reduces my anxiety and who doesn't like a little snack while they're getting tortured? It's important though that you maintain an angry stare, refuse to cooperate and stay as rigid as possible even while enjoying your snack. Don't let them see you enjoy the snack even for a second. They must believe at

all times that you'll never forgive them.
#AndYouWont

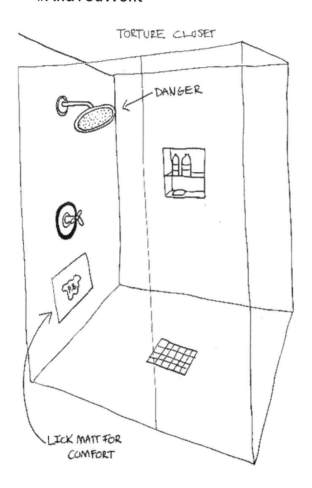

love hurts

I'VE ALLUDED TO THE NEED for strategic retaliation techniques in several chapters. It pains me to say this, but sometimes you have to do what you have to do. Why not enjoy it a little? **#ThisHurtsMeMoreThanItHurtsYou #ThatsALie**

In this chapter, we'll look at ways you can send a clear message that something the hoomans have done or not done was not to your liking. It follows the chapter on baffs for a reason. **#HintHint** You must maintain your standards or you'll find yourself sleeping on the floor, uncovered, unclothed and un-pampered. **#Unacceptable**

One important factor in conveying the message clearly is timeliness. You must execute your retaliation within a short amount of time after the infraction or they won't understand the two are related. **#RememberTheyAreMorons**

Consider these options as ways to get your point across:

- **Everyone poops**: And you can do it wherever and whenever you want! Retaliation poops require a surgical approach and you have to decide which one is right for you. There are two main types of retaliation poop. One is the "when did this happen?" method and the other is the "look them dead in the lookers" method.

"When did this happen?" is what your hooman will yell upon discovering your hidden poop pile. Try to hide it behind something or under something so they smell it before they see it. Again, carpet or fabric surfaces are better. If things have gone really off the rails in your training, you can leave it in the hooman's bed, but this should really be a last resort. **#TheyAreSensitiveAboutTheirBeds** This method is best used when trying to remind the hoomans that you have all the power. When they need a little reminder that you can poop anywhere at any time.

The "look them dead in the lookers" method has already been discussed in a previous chapter. It's important that this style be used immediately following an incident of misbehavior. You have to halp them understand what they are in trouble for or the technique is meaningless.

- **Destroy things**: Destroying stuff is always a clear way to send a message. Your choice point really is around what to destroy. The lowest level of destruction is to destroy something unimportant, like a toilet paper roll, a brown bag or a little drywall.

The next level up is using a toy to send your message. Shredding and de-squeaking a toy shows your power and strength, but in a passive-aggressive way. Could I do this to you, hooman? **#YesICould** Will I? **#YaNeverKnow**

Moving up in the destruction elevator, we find ourselves at the "something they value" floor. Choosing wisely here is important. If you choose something too valuable, things can turn ugly and you'll have to hear about it for years. "Remember when you ate my grandmother's diamond ring, you jerk?" "Remember when you destroyed the wedding cake?" **#TheyNeverLetThingsGo** Pick something they don't use every day and they seem to treat differently. It halps if you can pick something specific to the hooman who has violated your sacred trust with their infraction. An expensive bra, purse or shirt is a great way to communicate with the female full-sized hooman. Not the cheap stretchy bra that looks comfortable. Get the one that's lacy and cushioned with extra stuff. Those get way more attention during yelling. For purses, I try to just damage the strap so they don't notice at first and everything falls out when they grab it to go. **#LaughsForHours** For shirts, apply the bra rule. It can't be a shirt they wear every day. It needs to be a shirt with no words or drawings on it. Look for a tag that says, "dry clean only." I wish they'd only "dry-clean" me. **#ButIDigress**

For the male hoomans, I recommend focusing on tools, leather and video games. These seem to be all they really care about. Leave tools in usable condition but permanently marred with teefsmarks so they always remember you when they use it again. Chewing a hole or scratching up a leather chair like you're digging to China is another great attention-grabber. Every time he goes to relax in his comfy chair, he'll be reminded of your power and ferocity. Now, be very careful with video games. These are the most cherished items for my Daddy. Pick one to destroy that he hasn't played in a while. If you go too high-value he could come unglued and disown you. And never ever go for the actual Xbox. **#HeWillEndYou**

Note: see the next section for specific advice on maximizing shoe carnage for optimal effect.

Other note: try to resist destroying items that belong to the value-sized and fun-sized hoomans. Their sirens go off and mayhem ensues.
#ItsNotWorthTheHeadache

- **Shoes**: I don't know why, but shoes seem to be very important to the hoomans. These are the covers hoomans put on their feets because they are too delicate to survive in the wild. You can use shoes in a variety of ways to deliver your message. You can always take a tier one approach and just move or hide the shoe to remind them you have this power. Tier two would involve leaving a little poop prezzie in a shoe. Tier three is, of course, total destruction of one shoe. If you're really steamed and need to send a louder message, destroy one shoe each from multiple sets. **(PRO-TIP: never destroy a matching pair.)**

creature comforts

LET'S FACE IT, we work hard. We work tirelessly to keep these hoomans alive and well. To train them and support them. We deserve some pampering. In this chapter, we will discuss some wonderful ways you can halp the hoomans halp you with these creature comforts.
#YouDeserveIt

- **Mani/Pedi spa treatment:** I like popping into the vet's office for a little paw pampering. Until recently, I'd get a  nail trim and a little topping off of the anal glands and that would be it. It's a nice enough time. I get attention, all the techs tell me how handsome I am, sometimes I get a squirt of spray cheese, I delight them with my charm and I head home. But lately Mommy has really upped her spa day game. When I get home, she cuddles me in the big comfy chair while she files my nails to remove any jagged bits and slathers my paws in Musher's Secret. **#HelloFootMassage #DontMindIfIDo** Sometimes I fall asleep during the foot rub part. And I have soft supple feets for weeks.

- **Hot towels**: Suffering the indignity and horror of baffs is awful. We all know it. But what if you could train your hoomans into a post-baff swaddle in a cocoon of warm towels? I've done it and so can you. Start by shivering your whole body as soon as you are free from the horrible baff. Shiver like you have no control over your body temperature and make sure your ears and lookers are in the aforementioned "I'm just an innocent puppy, why don't you love me?" position. Cuddle against the weakest hooman and shiver as they try to warm you. This make take a few times before they realize they can pre-heat the towels in the dryer for added comfort. It took me about three baffs to get them trained. Mommy pre-heats the towels in the dryer then sits ready to cocoon and swaddle me as soon as I launch from the baffroom. I crawl into her lap and let her wrap me up in warm cozy comfort and tell me she's sorry for the horrible thing Daddy just did to me. I'm working now on getting some treats added to this spa treatment. This should, of course, be obvious to her. But she's slow so we do

what we can.
#GoodThingShesSquishyAtLeast

- **Looker-boogies:** Another invaluable use for hoomans is boogie management. I find it halpful to pick one primary hooman to be responsible for boogie management and train them to your liking. Other hoomans can sub in from time to time, but it's best to have one that knows how to do it right. For daily looker-boogies management, I've worked out a nice morning ritual with my Mommy. After I scream, pounce or make fake vomit sounds to alert them it's time to get up, I enjoy a nice brekkie and a short walkie with Daddy. This is our nice alone time to talk man stuff and patrol the neighborhood for threats. Then I run back to the bedroom and jump on Mommy's face. **#SheLovesIt** I've trained her to sit up and make a space in her lap for me under the covers. She assumes the position, I assume the position, she covers me up to get warm and then she tends to my boogies. We talk about the agenda for the day and what I can expect in terms of adventures, snackies, and playdates. It's a nice way to spend a little quality alone time with her and set her day off on the right paw. **#AndIGetCleanLookers**

- **Jammies**: Look, some dogs might tell you that clothing on dogs is unnecessary or uncool. I'm here to tell you right now - they are wrong. Jammies, sweaters and hoodies are the best. I've managed to get Mommy to order me all manner of clothing and I love it all (except things on my feets; don't cover my feets, thanks.) It took a while for her to get the hang of sizing and to know which item I want for the day or night. But we have a good system now. I pick out my jammies each night: lightweight for spring and summer and fleece for fall and winter. They are so cozy and comforting. Some days I'm in a waffle Henley mood and some days I throw a bone to Daddy with my BEST FRIEND hoodie. They also provide added warmth during winter walkies. I also like the way Mommy laughs like an idiot when I choose the llama pajamas.
#ShesDimButAdorable

- **Blankies**: Similar to jammies, blankies are more of a necessity than an optional comfort. But, hoomans seem slow to pick up on this. I've trained my hoomans to station a Finn-sized blankie at each of my napping spots. I'm experiencing mixed results on getting them to notice I need covering up or uncovering. I haven't cracked the code on that yet. But, at least the blankies are there at the ready when they realize I need halp.

- **Camp/Play dates**: Sometimes hoomans forget how much we crave play time with our friends. I find that a few well-placed tantrums or "bad choices" can send a clear message that it's time for a day at camp or a play date with friends. Bad choices include: destroying one or more toys, pacing around the house like a cornered lion and howling or crying until they give in, destroying something they care about like a sofa or pillow, scratching at a painted door or wall, barking endlessly at nothing just to interrupt their work calls, pawing at their hands while they try to type, knocking their laptop or phone out of their hands, insisting on games of fetch (aka keep away) and other generally annoying behaviors that demonstrate you have energy and attitude to burn.

What's most important is for you to remember, YOU'RE WORTH IT. You deserve extra comforts to help you manage your own stress. Figure out what you like best and use all the strategies we've reviewed to get it!

initiating play

PLAY IS A WONDERFUL WAY to enrich your hooman both mentally and emotionally. In this chapter, we'll examine ways you can incorporate play into your training routine. #ForYouAndForThem

Playing with your hooman is a fun way to reinforce who's Alpha while also deepening your trust bond. Especially with toy-play. They get to feel like Alpha for a second, then you snatch it back and you're Alpha. You trust they will throw it and they trust you'll bring it back. It's all about teaching them how to make it the most fun possible for you.

- **I want you to want to touch it, but don't touch it**: Coveting our toys is the bestest most delightfulest  thing a hooman can do to increase their street value. Teach them to want the toy by putting it very close to their face, but snatching it away if they reach for it. Lose your mind if they grab it without your express permission.

- **Ok, you can touch it**: You'll need a way to signal when it's ok for them to touch a toy in order to proceed with tug, fetch, chase me or where'd it go? I usually drop the toy onto their hand to show it is time. #ItIsTheWay

- **Fetch (aka keep away)**: Fetch is a tricky one because I've heard around the water dish that some dogs actually want to fetch the ball and have it thrown again. **#Perplexing** I find I can tolerate only one throw and then I insist on stealing the ball and running away. #NoYOUFetchItHooman

- **Chase me**: Chase me is a classic good time. It's hard to go wrong with chase me, really. I get into the play position and encourage the hooman to take off with a toy. I then give chase and they usually try to trick me by turning back the way they came or hiding around a corner. Let them believe you're falling for that as 1) it delights them and 2) it extends play.

- **Where'd it go?**: Another good time is the old "Where'd it go? I don't know!" game. There's almost always a moment when you have to decide whether to just rip their arm off to get to the toy they're hiding behind their back. You'll be tempted. Don't do it. Just let the hooman believe you can't see it and it's a total mystery where it went. **#WhoKnows #DefinitelyNotYou**

- **What's under the covers and can I bite it?**: My hoomans like to play a game that triggers my hunting instinct. They put a squeaky toy under the covers and dart it around under there for me to try to catch. They dart left and I pounce. They zoom right and I pounce and bite. It's great fun for all of us. Mommy gets testy when I chew through the duvet cover though. **(PRO-TIP: don't start playing this game while they're asleep by assuming something you feel under the covers is a toy that needs biting.)** #IveLearnedThatLessonTheHardWay #SoHaveThey

- **No bites**: "No bites!!" remains a confusing but exhilarating game. However, it can only be played with Daddy. No one else. He and I wrastle around on the floor and I air bite in his general direction. Then he usually shoves his big meaty paw into my mouf for me to nibble on. This goes on for a while and Mommy occasionally yells, "No bites!" #ButIMustBite

wrap up

YOUR NOW HAVE all the tools you need to train, protect and manage your hoomans. Just remember:

1. They are a lot of work, but you can do it!
2. They are dim but adorable.
3. Consistency is key.
4. You are Alpha! **#Roar**
5. Frozen dairy slop is life.
6. They are worth it!
7. Seriously though about the frozen dairy slop.
8. Also, bacon.

CERTIFICATE OF COMPLETION

_____ HAS COMPLETED THE TRAINING NECESSARY TO BE TRUSTED WITH THE CARE AND PROTECTION OF THEIR HOOMANS AND HEREBY PROMISES TO NEVER GIVE IN TO THEIR MADNESS.

_____
(YOU PAW HERE)

I hope you'll try some of these techniques and let me know how they work out for you. Stay strong out there, doggos. The hoomans are counting on us.

keep the fun going

TO LEARN MORE ABOUT ME and my other hilarious books, check out my media coverage, how we donate time to schools and how to follow me for daily fun on social media, scan this barcode with your phone or go to www.linktr.ee/gwenromack and have fun exploring!

And **don't forget to check out the Field Guide Companion page** on my website. <u>There you can find</u> pictures and videos of my use of these techniques with my hoomans. **THE SECRET PASSWORD IS #imwithfinn**
https://thefinnchronicles.com/field-guide
#SpoilerAlertImAdorable

acknowledgements

FINN WANTS TO THANK a few key people and organizations. A huge thanks to the Vizsla- and Beagle-loving communities on Facebook, friends and other authors that have followed Finn's updates from the beginning, encouraged us, given us advice during training struggles, sent us surprise packages, and kept nudging me to publish.

Most importantly. . . the rescues! Vizslas, in particular, are sensitive and intense dogs that need special owners and special support when in rescue. Their emotional nature makes the inconsistency and fear of unstable situations especially traumatic. Finn hopes you'll consider volunteering for or donating to the rescues listed below to help save dogs just like him. If every reader donates just $5, imagine how many dogs can be helped! We personally know, love and trust the dedicated heroes at:

Airsong's Angels, Inc. is an all-volunteer, 501(c)3 non-profit organization and Georgia State Licensed Animal Rescue dedicated to improving the lives of the

vizslas in their care by bringing them current on vaccinations, attending to their medical and behavioral needs, providing for spay/neuter and carefully rehoming them into loving, furever families.
https://airsongsangelsinc.org/

Cane Rosso Rescue is a Dallas, TX, based 501(c)3 non-profit organization dedicated to raising funds and building awareness for dogs in need of homes in Texas. The goal of Cane Rosso Rescue is to find homes for dogs that have been abandoned at shelters or whose owners can no longer care for them. They are looking for fosters, adopters and volunteers to help transport dogs to their future homes. Donations are accepted via Paypal to rescue@canerosso.com to assist with medical care and other expenses that come with saving these dogs.
https://www.canerossorescue.org/

Colorado/Wyoming Vizsla Rescue Group, Inc. is a 501(c)3 non-profit organization and Colorado State Licensed Animal Rescue officially formed in 2007. Their mission is to protect the Vizsla who has been abandoned or abused. They offer additional support to humane shelters or animal rescue organizations that handle stray or surrendered Vizslas in need of care due to natural disasters or other emergencies. Their coverage area includes Colorado, Wyoming, western Kansas, western Nebraska and New Mexico, but they generously assist and support other states when the need arises. https://www.coloradovizsla.org/

Conestoga Vizsla Club (CVC) New Beginnings is a Virginia-based non-profit rescue group that halps Vizslas in need, primarily in the Virginia, Maryland, Delaware, and Washington D.C. region. https://cvcweb.org/Rescue

about the author

Finn's dutiful transcriber, Gwen Romack (aka The Squishy One), is a Maryland native, avid dog lover and rescue volunteer.

Gwen and her husband Evan (aka The Hairy One) agreed to foster Finn a year after losing their beloved Vizsla/Pit mix, Mr. Snuggles, at age

14. She began posting Finn's weekly updates on Facebook as a way to help prospective adopters fall in love with Finn. However, it was clear pretty quickly that she and her husband would become foster fails. Finn was already home! The posts became so popular in the Vizsla community that she decided to continue his weekly updates on the frustrations of a dog rescuing his difficult hoomans.

In 2020, the books were turned into *The Finn Chronicles* series that each catalogue a year in Finn's life and adventures. As Finn's popularity grew and the books took off, Finn's fans started asking for more. Finn now guest-teaches to littles all over the country via Zoom and has started writing new books like this one. Finn and Gwen love hearing the stories from fans of all ages about how much joy he brings them.

At the time of publishing, sweet and sassy Finn is in year three of weekly updates. If the books do well, Gwen plans to keep publishing subsequent years and donate a portion of the proceeds to Finn's favorite rescue organizations.

Made in the USA
Columbia, SC
08 February 2021